EXPLORE
Geography Picture Dictionary

BALLARD & TIGHE
PUBLISHERS

Brea, California

AUTHORS

Carin Dewhirst, M.Ed., is a graduate of Occidental College, California and Columbia University, New York. She has written eight children's books, including adaptions of *Peter and the Wolf* and *The Nutcracker*, as well as *My Tricks and Treats*, *Lullabies and Bedtime Stories*, and *Strike Up the Orchestra!: A Guide to Classical Music for Children*. She is a co-author of *Explore America* and contributor to *Explore the Ancient World*.

Leila A. Langston, B.A., is a graduate of Occidental College, California. She has extensive teaching experience and also has served as a learning specialist and ESL program coordinator. Langston is the author of *Carousel of IDEAS*, *Explore the Ancient World*, and *Explore the United States*, and co-author of *IDEAS for Literature* and *Explore America*.

Roberta Stathis, Ph.D., is an educator, writer, and editor. She received a bachelor of arts degree with honors in anthropology and social sciences and a master of arts degree in education from California State University, San Bernardino. She earned a Ph.D. in education from the Claremont Graduate University. Stathis is the author of *Explore World History* and served as editor of *Explore America*, *Explore the Ancient World*, and *Explore the United States*. She is also the author of a children's book, *Lost: One Dad!*

GENERAL GEOGRAPHY EDITOR

Mark P. Kumler is an Associate Professor of Geography at California State University, San Bernardino. He has fond memories of drawing maps of faraway places in school. He studied geography at Dartmouth College, Michigan State University, and the University of California at Santa Barbara, and he has traveled extensively throughout Europe, New Zealand, and North America. He enjoys teaching geography to his children with maps, globes, and books like this.

REVIEWERS

The authors and publisher express grateful appreciation to the teachers and other educators who carefully reviewed the *Explore Geography Picture Dictionary* and provided helpful comments and suggestions:

Suzanne M. Hidalgo, San Bernardino City Unified School District, Highland, California

Erik B. Johansen, Oxnard Union High School District, Oxnard, California

Martha J. Kemp, Phoenix Union High School District, Glendale, Arizona

Conrad Nicoll, California State University, Fullerton, California

Paul Watlington, Falls Church High School District, Falls Church, Virginia

PHOTO & ILLUSTRATION CREDITS

(t=top, b=bottom, c=center)

Page: 5, (b) Paul Helmle; 6, (c) Sabrina Lammé; 7, (c) Emmy Rhee (b) Courtesy of Grand Canyon Explorer, www.kaibab.org; 8, (t) Tom Sullivan, www.geocities.com/Paris/4118/index.html (b) Keith Neely; 14, (c) Emmy Rhee; 15, (t) Emmy Rhee; 16, (b) Heera Kang; 17, (b) Donald Schwert, Department of Geosciences, North Dakota State University; 18, (t) Keith Neely (c) Michelle Chew (b) Marvin J. Malecha, FAIA; 19, (t) Emmy Rhee (b) Sabrina Lammé; 20, (t) Aileen Buckley; 21, (b) Keith Neely; 24, (t) Leilani Trollinger; 25, (t) Emmy Rhee; 27, (b) Patricia P. Miller; 28, (b) Elaine Elwell; 29, (c) Library of Congress; 31, (t) Emmy Rhee; 32, (c) Dover Publications; 33, (b) Keith Neely; 36, (t) Emmy Rhee (b) Courtesy of Grand Canyon Explorer, www.kaibab.org; 39, (t) Erik Jones, Esq. (b) Emmy Rhee; 40, (b) Visuals Unlimited, Inc.; 42, (t) John Oswalt, www.jao.com; 43, (b) Emmy Rhee; 45, (c) Jim De Forge; 46, (t) Dorothy Roberts; 47, (t) Emmy Rhee (b) Twila Bing; 48, (c) Emmy Rhee (b) Sabrina Lammé; 49, (t) Emmy Rhee; 50, (t) Keith Neely

Every effort has been made to trace the copyright holders, and we apologize in advance for any omissions. We would be pleased to insert the appropriate acknowledgment in any subsequent edition of this book.

An IDEA® Content Resource from Ballard & Tighe

Managing Editor: Laurie Regan
Associate Editor: Heera Kang
Program Consultants: David Brisco, Leonor Morris, Patrice Sonberg
Editorial Assistant: Allison Mangrum
Art Director: Kathy Spear
Desktop Publishing Coordinator: Kathleen Styffe
Graphic Designer: Charles W. Shaffer, III

2001 Printing
ISBN 1-55501-489-5   Catalog #2-440

480 Atlas Street • Brea, CA 92821 • (800) 321-4332 • www.ballard-tighe.com • e-mail: info@ballard-tighe.com

Contents

Introduction 4

Geographical Features &
Terms from A to Z 5

Appendixes 51-54

    Appendix I: Geographical Features
       and Terms in Spanish 51

    Appendix II: Political Map of the United States . .52

    Appendix III: Relief Map of the United States . . .53

    Appendix IV: World Map & Statistics 54

A Note to Teachers and Parents 55

    Internet Links to Geography Activities 55

Index 56

Introduction

Can You Pronounce *Archipelago*?

Can you name the tallest mountain in the world? Do you know what a gazetteer is? Do you know why the Dead Sea is "dead"? The *Explore Geography Picture Dictionary* answers all of these questions and more! Look inside and you will find places, names, facts, and figures that will help you understand the world. And the more you know, the more you will realize that the earth is an amazing place.

All of the information in the *Explore Geography Picture Dictionary* is easy to find and easy to understand. Everything is arranged in alphabetical order. For example, *archipelago* is a snap to find: it's between *aqueduct* and *atlas*.

The **pronunciation guide** is right after the word. This is a special spelling that shows you how to say the word. The hyphens (-) tell where the word is divided into syllables or units of sound. The syllable in all capital letters, "PEL" in this case, is the part of the word to stress.

archipelago: (ar-kuh-PEL-uh-goh) *n.* A large group of islands. The Japanese archipelago includes four main islands and more than 4,000 smaller islands.

The **definition** tells what the word means. If one of the words in the definition is printed in red (such as islands here), then there is an entry in this dictionary for that word as well. Sometimes there are examples in parentheses after the letters "e.g." This abbreviation ("e.g.") comes from two Latin words, *exempli gratia*, that mean "for example."

For more information, read the sentence after the definition. **Reading a word in a sentence** can help you understand its meaning.

A **colorful map, photograph, or drawing** shows you a picture of each geographical term. For example, this map shows a picture of an archipelago.

Who Said, "No Man Is an Island"?

You'll find the answer in one of the many **Voices in Geography** sections. These quotations relate to geography and are from famous people. By the way, John Donne wrote, "No man is an island" about 400 years ago.

Want more facts? The **Fun Facts** tell you interesting things about the world. Did you know that Greenland is the largest island in the world?

The *Explore Geography Picture Dictionary* is designed to help you learn about our amazing world.

Geographical Features & Terms from A to Z

agriculture, industry, and resources map: (AG-rih-kul-chur, IHN-dus-tree, and REE-sor-sez map) *n.* A map that shows the crops, industries, and natural resources of an area. This agriculture, industry, and resources map shows four major areas where people make steel and iron.

LEGEND

AGRICULTURE, INDUSTRY, AND RESOURCES

■ Hay and Dairy Cattle	■ Corn	■ Wheat
■ Tobacco	■ Cotton	■ Rice
■ Sugar Cane	▽ Range Cattle	⌐ Mining
⊔ Iron and Steel Making	✖ Textile Manufacturing	⊏⊐ Flour Milling

aqueduct: (AK-wuh-dukt) *n.* A bridge or other structure that helps move water in a certain direction. This aqueduct was built more than 1,000 years ago by the ancient Romans. See IRRIGATION SYSTEMS.

▼ FUN FACTS ▼

Romans were the first people to build aqueducts. By A.D. 97, aqueducts brought 85 million gallons of water into Rome in one day. That's enough water to fill 850 large swimming pools every day.

archipelago: (ar-kuh-PEL-uh-goh) *n.* A large group of islands. The Japanese archipelago includes four main islands and more than 4,000 smaller islands.

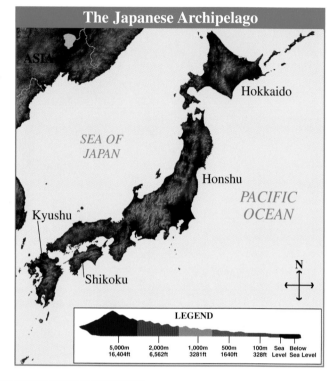

The Japanese Archipelago

ASIA

Hokkaido

SEA OF JAPAN

Honshu

PACIFIC OCEAN

Kyushu

Shikoku

N

LEGEND

5,000m 16,404ft | 2,000m 6,562ft | 1,000m 3281ft | 500m 1640ft | 100m 328ft | Sea Level | Below Sea Level

▼ FUN FACTS ▼

Abraham Cresques created the Catalan Atlas in the late 1300s as a gift for the king of France. This atlas described the riches of South Africa where gold "grew like carrots."

ATLAS

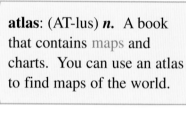

atlas: (AT-lus) *n.* A book that contains maps and charts. You can use an atlas to find maps of the world.

bay: (bay) *n.* A part of the ocean going into the land. As this map shows, many rivers flow into Chesapeake Bay.

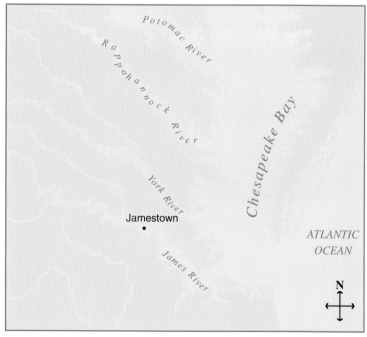

Potomac River

Rappahannock River

Chesapeake Bay

York River

Jamestown

ATLANTIC OCEAN

James River

N

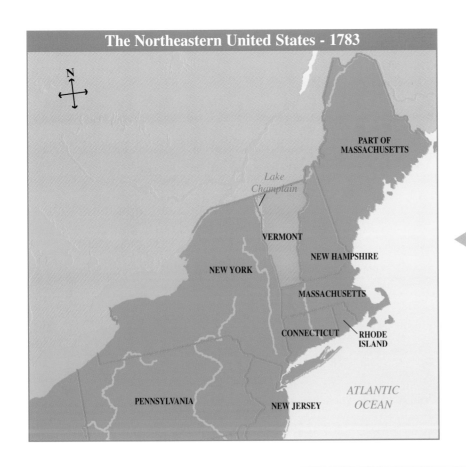

The Northeastern United States - 1783

N

PART OF
MASSACHUSETTS

Lake
Champlain

VERMONT

NEW HAMPSHIRE

NEW YORK

MASSACHUSETTS

CONNECTICUT   RHODE
ISLAND

ATLANTIC
OCEAN

PENNSYLVANIA

NEW JERSEY

boundary: (BOWN-duh-ree) *n.* A line marking the border between two areas. This map of the United States in 1783 shows that Lake Champlain forms part of Vermont's western boundary.

canal: (kuh-NAL) *n.* A ditch or other waterway dug into the ground to carry the flow of water. Farmers sometimes use canals to bring water to their fields. See IRRIGATION SYSTEMS.

canal

canyon: (KAN-yun) *n.* A deep, narrow valley. You can see a river at the bottom of this canyon.

🌏 *Voices in Geography* 🌏

"Geography is the study of earth as the home of people."

—Yi-Fu Tuan, 1991

> **cape**: (kayp) *n.* A narrow piece of land that sticks out into a sea or other body of water; similar to a peninsula, only smaller. Prince Henry of Portugal studied navigation at Cape St. Vincent.

> **cataract**: (KAT-uh-rackt) *n.* A large waterfall or steep rapids The cataracts of the Nile River are steep rapids.

▽ FUN FACTS ▽

The second cataract of the Nile River is now under the waters of Lake Nassar. Lake Nassar was created when the Aswan High Dam was built in 1970.

HOW A CAVE IS MADE

1. Water dissolves limestone. It makes an underground cave.

2. The water level drops, leaving the cave dry.

3. Rocks fall and cover the mouth of the cave.

cave: (kayv) *n.* An opening in a hillside. The drawing (left) shows how a cave is made. The picture (below) shows a photograph of a cave.

channel: (CHAN-ul) *n.* A wide passage of water joining two larger bodies of water. The waterway that separates Great Britain and the European mainland is called the English Channel. See STRAIT

city: (SIT-ee) *n.* A place where people live that is larger and has more people than a town or village. A city has many buildings and roads.

cliff: (klif) *n.* A high, steep rock. This photograph shows a very steep cliff.

climate: (KLY-mut) *n.* The long-term, average weather conditions. The map below shows three major types of climate—tropical (hot), temperate (mild), and polar (very cold).

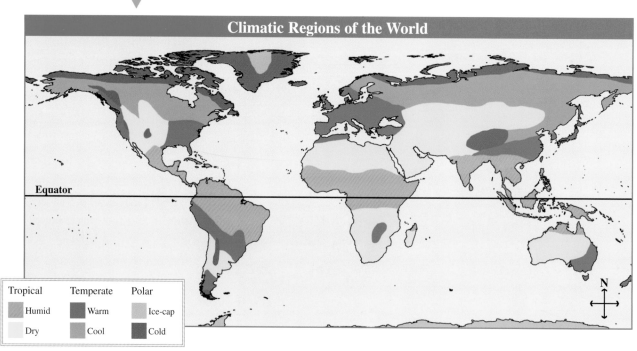

Climatic Regions of the World

Equator

Tropical	Temperate	Polar
Humid	Warm	Ice-cap
Dry	Cool	Cold

N

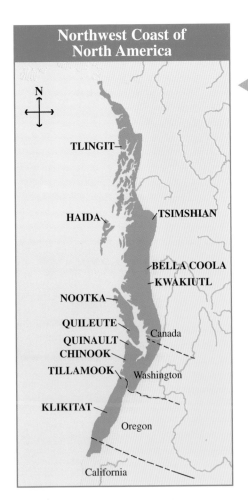

N

TLINGIT—

HAIDA—   —TSIMSHIAN

—BELLA COOLA
—KWAKIUTL

NOOTKA—

QUILEUTE—
QUINAULT—   Canada
CHINOOK—
TILLAMOOK—   Washington

KLIKITAT—

Oregon

California

coast: (kohst) *n.* The land along the water. Many American Indian tribes settled along the Northwest Coast of North America.

commercial harbor: (kuh-MUR-shul HAR-bur) *n.* A harbor with docks and other facilities so that ships can load and unload their cargo. This picture shows a busy commercial harbor in Hawaii.

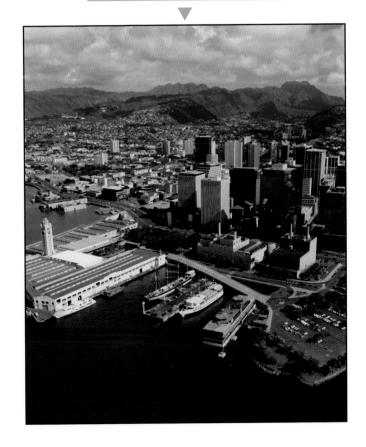

compass rose: (KUM-pus rohz) *n.* A symbol on a map that shows directions such as north, south, east, and west. Most maps include a compass rose. It can be very simple or very elaborate.

N
W   E
S

FUN FACTS

People have used the compass rose symbol since the 1300s. Its name comes from the similarity of the compass points to the petals of a rose.

continent: (KAHN-tuh-nent) *n.* One of the seven major landmasses of the earth—Africa, Antarctica, Asia, Australia, Europe, North America, and South America. Asia is the largest continent on earth.

▼ FUN FACTS ▼

Antarctica is the coldest, windiest, and driest continent on earth.

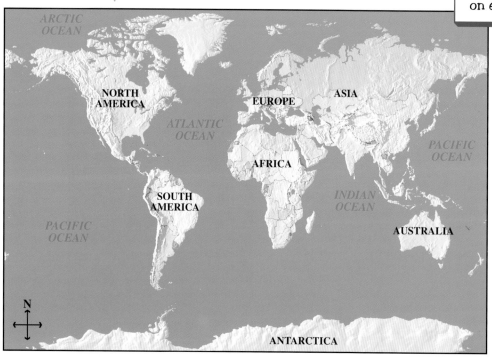

Continental Divide: (KAHN-tuh-nent-ul duh-VYD) *n.* The ridge of the Rocky Mountains that separates rivers flowing toward the Atlantic Ocean from those flowing toward the Pacific Ocean. All the rivers to the west of the Continental Divide flow toward the Pacific Ocean. All the rivers to the east flow toward the Atlantic Ocean.

12

dam: (dam) *n.* Something (a barrier) built across a waterway to control the flow or raise the level of water. People build dams for many reasons, including to prevent flooding. See IRRIGATION SYSTEMS

point located at 45°N, 30°E

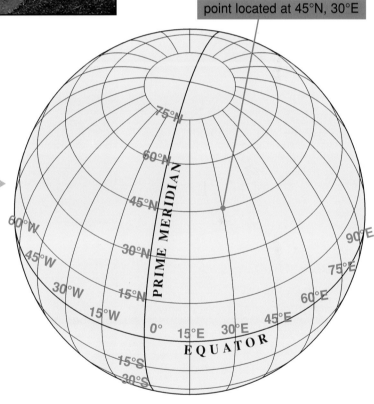

degree: (di-GREE) *n.* A unit of measurement used to describe latitude or longitude The symbol is a raised circle, so 45° is "forty-five degrees." Sailors keep track of their location by knowing their degree of latitude and longitude. See EQUATOR and PRIME MERIDIAN. (Units of degrees are used to describe other measurements including temperature.)

delta: (DEL-tuh) *n.* A deposit of sand and soil at the mouth of some rivers. A delta is usually shaped like a triangle. The delta of the Nile River has rich and fertile soil.

demographic change: (dehm-uh-GRAF-ik chayng) *n.* A change in the size, distribution (e.g., where people live), or composition (e.g., age, gender, or ethnicity) of a population. This chart shows a large demographic change. In the 50-year period between 1870 and 1920, many Americans moved to urban areas.

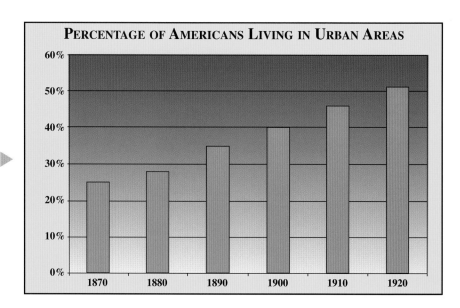

PERCENTAGE OF AMERICANS LIVING IN URBAN AREAS

depth: (depth) *n.* The distance from sea level to the bottom of an ocean, sea, lake, or other body of water. Scientists measure the depth of oceans with scientific instruments.

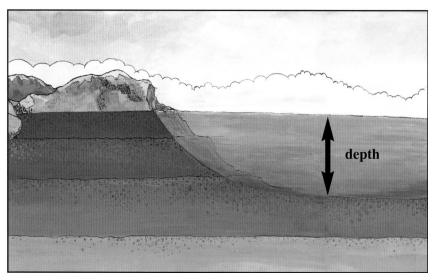

depth

desert: (DEZ-urt) *n.* A region of the earth that gets very little rainfall (fewer than 10 inches per year) and has extreme hot and cold temperatures. The Sahara desert has no trees and very little plant or animal life.

 FUN FACTS

The Sahara desert is the largest desert in the world.

14

DIP-SLIP FAULT **LATERAL FAULT**

THRUST FAULT **TEAR FAULT**

earthquake: (URTH-kwayk) *n.* A movement in the earth's surface caused by shifting tectonic plates or volcanic activity. This drawing shows four different kinds of faults. When the earth's surface moves along a fault, it causes an earthquake.

22,834 feet

elevation: (el-uh-VAY-shun) *n.* A word that describes the height of mountains and other natural features; elevation is usually measured in feet or meters using sea level (which is 0 elevation) as the starting point. The Andes Mountains reach elevations of more than 22,000 feet.

 FUN FACTS

The Andes in South America are the second tallest mountains in the world. Did you know that potatoes can grow on the Andes at higher than 10,000 feet?

environmental pollution: (en-VY-run-ment-ul puh-LOO-shun) **n.** Contamination of the earth's water, air, or soil. These factories put chemicals into the air, causing environmental pollution.

equator: (ih-KWAY-tur) **n.** An imaginary line that goes around the middle of the earth. The area north of the equator is in the Northern Hemisphere and the area south of the equator is in the Southern Hemisphere. The latitude of the equator is 0°. Because the equator runs through the middle of Africa, part of the African continent is in the Northern Hemisphere and part is in the Southern Hemisphere.

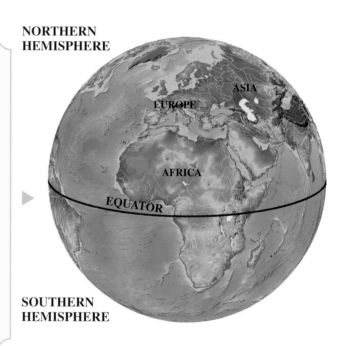

NORTHERN HEMISPHERE

ASIA

EUROPE

AFRICA

EQUATOR

SOUTHERN HEMISPHERE

erosion: (ee-ROH-zhun) **n.** The wearing away of soil material from the earth's surface. Erosion can be a serious problem for farmers.

🌎 *Voices in Geography* 🌎

"Geography will aim to make clear the relationships existing between natural environments and the distribution and activities of man."

—Harland H. Barrows, 1923

Fertile Crescent: (FURT-ul KREZ-ent) *n.* A region of rich, fertile soil that stretches from the Mediterranean Sea, between the Tigris and Euphrates rivers, to the Persian Gulf. Many ancient civilizations began in the Fertile Crescent.

flood plain: (flud playn) *n.* A flat area of land that is covered by water when the rivers or streams in the area overflow. Living on a flood plain can be dangerous if the nearby rivers overflow.

foothill: (FOOT-hill) *n.* A low hill at the bottom of a mountain. The small hills at the bottom of these tall mountains are called foothills. See PIEDMONT.

forest: (FOR-ist) *n.* A large area of land covered with trees and thick brush. During the Middle Ages, people of Europe cut down many forests so they could plant crops on the land.

frontier: (fruhn-TIHR) *n.* The part of a country that borders another country or an undeveloped region. The Chinese built the Great Wall to protect their frontier from invaders.

gap: (gap) *n.* A steep, narrow pass through a hill or mountain. A gap is made by wind or water. See MOUNTAIN PASS and RAVINE.

gap

gazetteer: (gaz-uh-TIHR) *n.* A geographical dictionary that includes brief descriptions about places. You can look in a gazetteer to find information about the place where you live.

 FUN FACTS

The first gazetteer was published in 1693 and was called "The Newsman's Interpreter: Being a Geographical Index."

19

geographer: (jee-OG-ruh-fur) *n.* A person who studies geography. People who want to be geographers go to college to learn about the earth and its features. This photograph shows geographers using a tool to collect information.

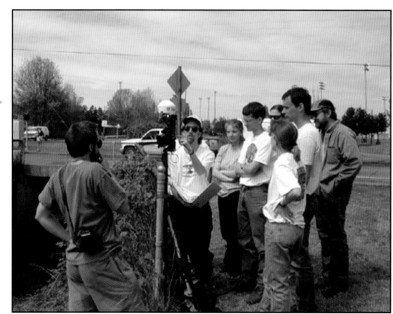

geography: (jee-OG-ruh-fee) *n.* The study of the earth and its features. Geography also includes the study of how people interact with their environment. This chart shows five themes of geography—place, location, people and environment, movement, and regions.

Regions

American Southwest

5 Themes of Geography

Movement

Place

Location

People and Environment

glacier: (GLAY-shur) *n.* A large mass of ice and snow that forms faster than the snow can melt. Sometimes people think of glaciers as rivers of ice. This glacier is in Alaska. There are more than 100,000 glaciers in Alaska.

 FUN FACTS

If you visit the New York Public Library, you can see one of the earliest globes. It was made in 1503. This globe even includes America because Columbus had just made his historic trip there.

globe: (glohb) *n.* A sphere (ball) that is a tiny model of the earth; it shows all the earth's land and water. A globe has many advantages over a flat map.

gorge: (gorj) *n.* A deep, narrow pass with steep sides. Archaeologists found fossil bones in Olduvai Gorge in Africa.

Great Lakes: (grayt laykz) *n.* The five lakes—Huron, Ontario, Michigan, Erie, and Superior—located on either side of the U.S. and Canadian border. The Great Lakes are the largest group of freshwater lakes in the world.

gulf: (gulf) *n.* A large area of sea or ocean partly enclosed by land. The city of Venice is located on the Gulf of Venice.

harbor: (HAHR-bur) *n.* A sheltered part of a body of water that is a safe place for ships. Plymouth Harbor looks small compared to the Atlantic Ocean, but it can hold many large ships. See COMMERCIAL HARBOR and PORT.

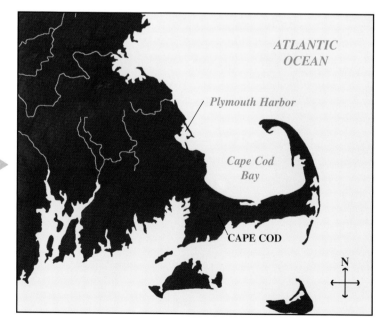

Voices in Geography 🌐

"I am not born for one corner; the whole world is my native land."
—Lucius Annaeus Seneca the Younger (4 B.C.–A.D. 65)

hemisphere: (HEM-uh-sfir) *n.* Half a sphere (ball). The world is divided into the northern and southern halves by the equator. It is also divided into the eastern and western halves by the prime meridian. Africa is located in all four hemispheres.

hill: (hill) *n.* Land that is higher than the ground around it. A hill is like a mountain, only smaller. See FOOTHILL and PIEDMONT.

The Earth's Hemispheres

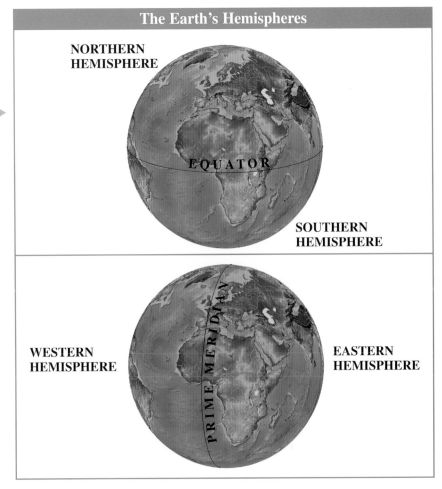

NORTHERN HEMISPHERE

EQUATOR

SOUTHERN HEMISPHERE

WESTERN HEMISPHERE

PRIME MERIDIAN

EASTERN HEMISPHERE

"…[The] study of geography forces one to consider the whole earth, it forces comparisons between countries, and people, and cultures."

—*Christian Science Monitor*, 1919

inlet: (IN-let) *n.* A narrow stream of water that goes inland from an ocean, river, or lake. Native Americans in the Pacific Northwest traveled in canoes over inlets.

international date line: (in-tur-NASH-un-ul dayt lyn) *n.* An imaginary line that begins at the North Pole and then goes through the Pacific Ocean to the South Pole. By international agreement, the calendar date is one day earlier in the area to the east of the international date line.

FUN FACTS

All the world has agreed that the international date line is where travelers change dates. When we travel eastward, we subtract a day. When we travel westward, we add a day.

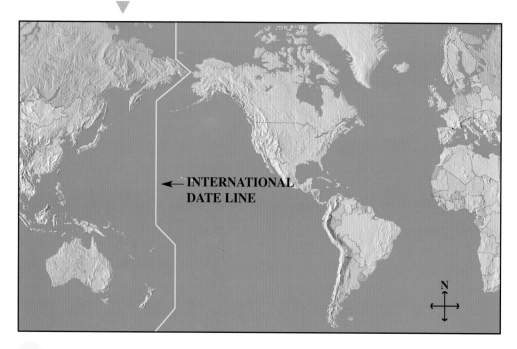

← INTERNATIONAL DATE LINE

N

"…[Japan] contains no fewer than 7,444 islands, mostly inhabited…"

—Marco Polo, 1299

irrigation systems: (ir-rih-GAY-shun SIS-tumz) *n.* Methods to supply land with water, including dams, canals, and aqueducts. Farmers use irrigation systems to bring water to their fields.

island: (I-lund) *n.* A piece of land surrounded completely by water. Some islands are called "continental islands" because they are pieces of a continent that have been separated from the mainland (e.g., Great Britain is a continental island). Some islands are called "oceanic islands" because they were formed by volcanoes on the ocean floor (e.g., the Hawaiian Islands are oceanic islands). This map shows one large island and several smaller ones. See ISLE and ARCHIPELAGO

FUN FACTS

In geography, the main difference between an island and a continent is size. But there is a big difference in size! The largest island is Greenland. But the largest continent, Asia, is 22 times larger than Greenland. In fact, Asia includes a third of the entire world's land area!

25

🌐 *Voices in Geography* 🌐

"Those who contemplate the beauty of the earth find reserves of strength that will endure as long as life lasts."

—Rachel Louise Carson (1907-1964)

isle: (I'LL) *n.* A small island; a piece of land surrounded completely by water. There are many isles along the coast of Great Britain. See ARCHIPELAGO.

Great Britain

isthmus: (ISS-muss) *n.* A narrow strip of land that connects two larger pieces of land. The United States built a canal across the Isthmus of Panama.

Isthmus of Panama

lake: (layk) *n.* A body of water that has land all around it. People settle near lakes because of the water, which supports plant and animal life.

"The kingdom [of Mali in Africa] is square in shape, being four months [of travel] in length and at least that much in breadth."

—Ibn Battuta, 1354

land bridge: (land bridj) *n.* A piece of land that connects two pieces of land. During the ice ages, the water level in the oceans dropped to expose land and this made land bridges. Experts think the earliest people in North America came across a land bridge from Asia during the ice ages. This land bridge is now covered with water and is called the Bering Strait.

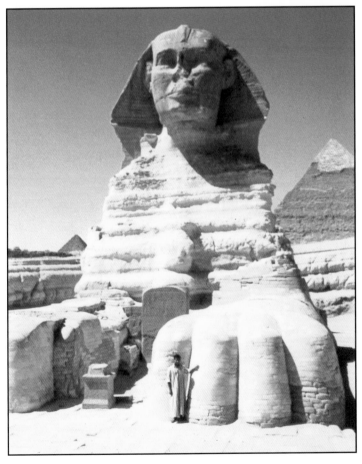

landmark: (LAND-mark) *n.* A large, natural feature (such as a mountain) or cultural feature (such as a building). Landmarks can help people locate places. The Great Sphinx serves as a landmark for travelers in Egypt.

landmass: (LAND-mass) *n.* A very large area of land, especially a continent. The continent of Africa is a huge landmass.

AFRICA

latitude: (LAT-uh-tood) *n.* The lines north and south of the equator used to measure distance. Lines of latitude are also called "parallels" because they are always the same distance apart. The equator is 0 degrees latitude. See LONGITUDE and PRIME MERIDIAN.

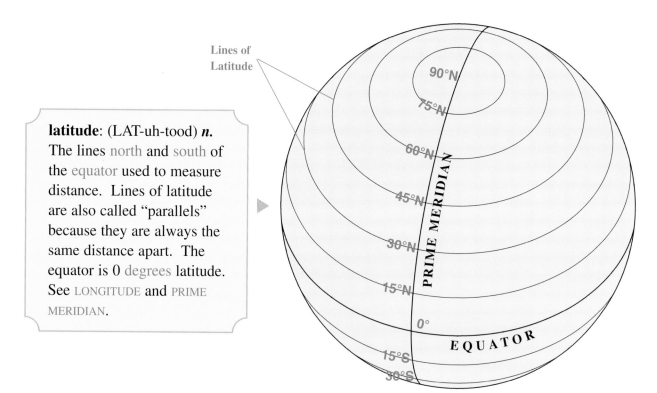

Lines of Latitude

90°N
75°N
60°N
45°N
30°N
15°N
0°
15°S
30°S

PRIME MERIDIAN

EQUATOR

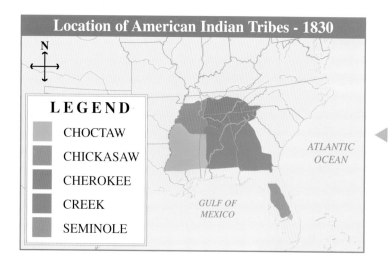

Location of American Indian Tribes - 1830

N

LEGEND
CHOCTAW
CHICKASAW
CHEROKEE
CREEK
SEMINOLE

ATLANTIC OCEAN

GULF OF MEXICO

legend: (LEJ-und) *n.* The words or symbols that explain how information is displayed on a map. A legend often is shown in a box on the map. Sometimes a legend is called a "key." Using the legend on this map, you can see the location of various American Indian tribes in 1830.

loess highlands: (LOH-ess HY-lundz) *n.* A high area above the North China Plain covered by deep layers of windblown yellow soil called loess. The Yellow River carries soil from the loess highlands to China's valleys and plains.

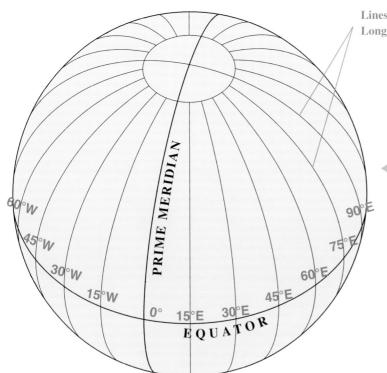

Lines of Longitude

PRIME MERIDIAN

EQUATOR

60°W 45°W 30°W 15°W 0° 15°E 30°E 45°E 60°E 75°E 90°E

longitude: (LON-juh-tood) *n.* The lines east and west of the prime meridian used to measure distance. Lines of longitude are also called meridians. Longitude is measured in degrees. The prime meridian is 0° longitude. See LATITUDE and PRIME MERIDIAN.

FUN FACTS

The Babylonians made the first known map of the world. About 900 B.C., they carved the tiny map into wet clay and dried it in the sun. The map is only about the size of a playing card.

map: (map) *n.* A picture or drawing of a region of the earth or the planets. This is a map of the world made in 1570. See AGRICULTURE, INDUSTRY, AND RESOURCES MAP, POLITICAL MAP, POPULATION MAP, RELIEF MAP, STREET MAP, and VEGETATION MAP.

marsh: (marsh) *n.* An area of low, wet land; a bog or swamp. A marsh is not a good place to grow crops.

mesa: (MAY-suh) *n.* A small area of high, flat land. Some American Indians settled on mesas in the Southwest region of North America. See PLATEAU.

mountain: (MOWN-tuhn) *n.* A very high, natural elevation of the earth's surface with steep sides; a very high hill. Early European settlers in America crossed mountains as they moved westward.

FUN FACTS

Mt. Everest is the tallest point on earth. It is part of the Himalaya Mountains in Asia. Mt. Everest is about 5½ miles above sea level.

"Mountains are earth's undecaying monuments."

—Nathaniel Hawthorne, 1868

mountain pass: (MOWN-tuhn pass) *n.* A gap (space) between mountains. Travelers are happy to find a mountain pass because it makes travel through tall mountains much faster. See GAP.

mountain range: (MOWN-tuhn raynj) *n.* A group of mountains forming a line. Mountain ranges affect the weather. Tall mountains catch winds and this results in rain.

31

🌎 *Voices in Geography* 🌎

"In our every deliberation, we must consider the impact of our decisions on the next seven generations."

—From the Great Law of the Iroquois Confederacy, c. 1450 A.D.

natural boundary: (NACH-ur-ul BOWN-duh-ree) *n.* Something natural (not made by human beings) such as a mountain range or river that marks the border or limit of an area. The Alps, the Pyrenees, and the Rhine River are natural boundaries of France. See BOUNDARY.

natural resources: (NACH-ur-ul REE-sor-sez) *n.* Forms of wealth that come from nature, including oil, water, and metals like gold and silver. The United States is a country with many natural resources such as gold.

north: (north) *n.* A direction indicating the area toward the North Pole. The area at the top of a map is usually north.

32

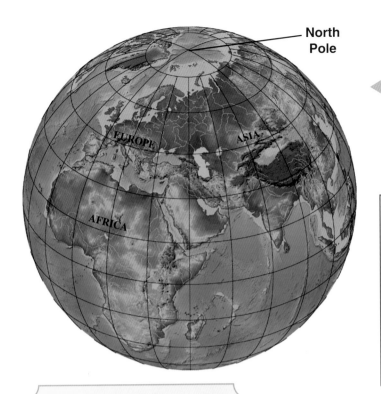

North Pole

North Pole: (north pohl) *n.*
The area at the top of the
earth; the North Pole is 90°
north of the equator.
Explorers first reached the
North Pole in 1909.

FUN FACTS

Who got there first? In April 1909, Admiral
Robert E. Peary reached the North Pole.
However, just a week before he returned to
civilization, another explorer, Frederick Cook,
claimed that he had reached the Pole in April
of 1908! After an investigation, Admiral
Peary was given the credit.

oasis: (oh-AY-sis) *n.* A place
in a desert that has water and
where plants can grow. Thirsty
travelers are happy to come
upon an oasis in the desert.

ocean: (OH-shun) **n.** A very large body of water. To help us find our way around the world, we have "divided" the water separating the continents into four oceans—the Pacific, the Atlantic, the Indian, and the Arctic. The United States is bordered by the Pacific Ocean on the west and the Atlantic Ocean on the east.

 FUN FACTS

Did you know that the Pacific Ocean is the largest ocean in the world? It covers about 64 million square miles. That's larger than all of the land in the world put together!

ocean currents: (OH-shun KUR-untz) **n.** Large amounts of water that move within or between oceans; generally, ocean currents flow clockwise in the Northern Hemisphere and counter clockwise in the Southern Hemisphere. Along the equator, ocean currents flow westward. Early European explorers followed ocean currents as they sailed toward the Americas. See TRADE WINDS.

EQUATOR

peninsula: (puh-NIN-suh-luh) **n.** A piece of land surrounded by water on three sides. There are many peninsulas in Europe, including the Scandinavian, the Iberian, and the Italian peninsulas.

ATLANTIC OCEAN

Scandinavian Peninsula

EUROPE

Iberian Peninsula

Italian Peninsula

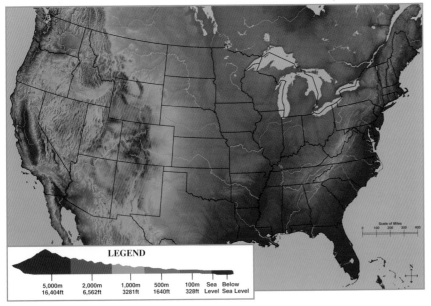

physical map (FIZ-uh-kul map) *n.* A map that shows the natural features of the earth's surface. There are two kinds of physical maps—relief maps and topographic maps. This physical map is a relief map of the United States.

LEGEND

| 5,000m 16,404ft | 2,000m 6,562ft | 1,000m 3281ft | 500m 1640ft | 100m 328ft | Sea Level | Below Sea Level |

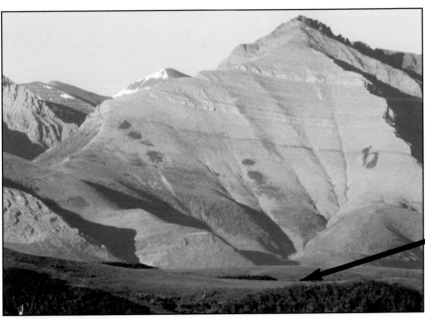

piedmont

piedmont: (PEED-mont) *n.* The area at the bottom of a mountain or highlands area. The Inca empire developed in the Andes region, which includes mountains and piedmont regions.

Inca Empire - c. early 1500s

SOUTH AMERICA

N

plain: (playn) *n.* A large piece of flat land. Most people in the world live on plains.

"In geography one must think about the size of the entire earth, as well as its shape, and its position under the heavens…"

—Ptolemy, c. A.D. 150

planet: (PLAN-ut) *n.* A large sphere (ball) in the sky that moves around a star in a circular pattern. In our solar system, the earth is the third planet from the sun.

plateau: (pla-TOH) *n.* A large area of high, flat land. America's Desert Southwest includes many plateaus. You can see many plateaus in this photograph of the Grand Canyon. See MESA.

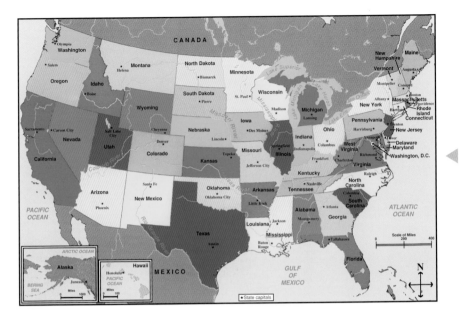

political map: (puh-LIHT-uh-kul map) *n.* A map that shows boundaries of states, countries, cities, and towns. This political map shows the United States of America.

population: (pahp-yoo-LAY-shun) *n.* All the people in a region, such as a country, city, or town. Every 10 years, we count the population of the United States to find out how many people live in the country.

 FUN FACTS

There are more than 6 billion people in the world today. Did you know that the population of the world increases by three people every second?

population map: (pahp-yoo-LAY-shun map) *n.* A map that shows the number of people living in a certain area. This population map shows the number of people who lived in America in 1910.

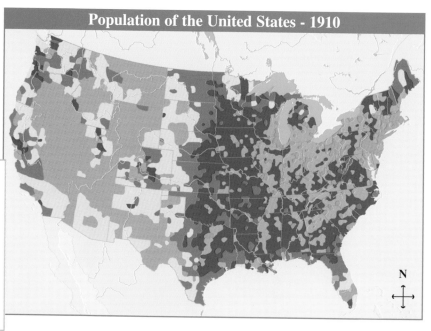

Population of the United States - 1910

People per square mile

Less than 5
5-15
15-45
45-120
120-225
More than 225

N

port: (port) *n.* A place on a waterway for ships to load or unload cargo. Ports often give ships and boats protection from storms and rough water. See HARBOR.

WESTERN HEMISPHERE

EASTERN HEMISPHERE

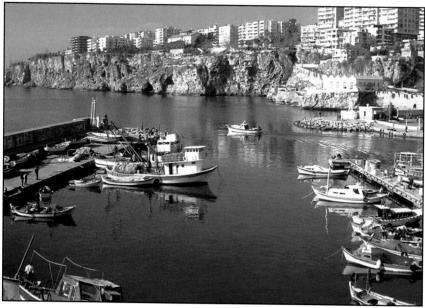

ASIA
EUROPE
AFRICA
PRIME MERIDIAN →

prime meridian: (prym muh-RID-ee-un) *n.* An imaginary line that begins at the North Pole and goes through Greenwich, England to the South Pole. The prime meridian divides the earth in half. The land to the west of the prime meridian is in the Western Hemisphere and the land to the east of it is in the Eastern Hemisphere. The prime meridian is at 0 degrees longitude. See LONGITUDE.

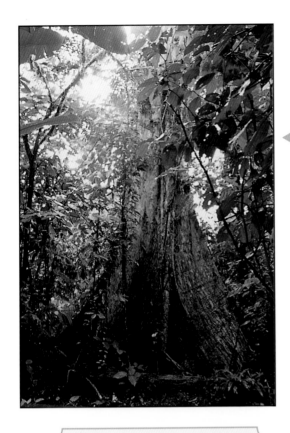

rain forest: (rayn FOR-ust) *n.* An evergreen forest in a tropical region that receives at least 100 inches of rain per year. The soil is usually thin and poor, but the vegetation is rich and thick. Some Maya kingdoms developed in the rain forests of Central America.

rapid: (RAP-id) *n.* A part of a river where the water moves swiftly. Rapids are usually caused by a narrowing of the river bed. During the early 1800s, American factory owners in the Northeast took advantage of rapids as a source of power for their machines. See CATARACT and WATERFALL.

ravine: (ruh-VEEN) *n.* A small, narrow valley with steep sides. A ravine is larger than a gully and smaller than a canyon. Ravines are usually made by running water. See GAP, GORGE, and MOUNTAIN PASS.

region: (REE-jun) *n.* An area or place; a specific part of the world. The region we call the American Southwest is made up of the states of Arizona, New Mexico, Oklahoma, and Texas.

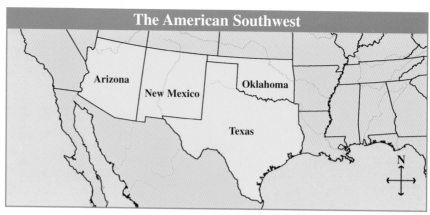

The American Southwest

Arizona

New Mexico

Oklahoma

Texas

N

relief map: (ree-LEEF map) *n.* A map that uses colors and shading to show the natural features (such as hills and valleys) of the earth. A relief map is one kind of physical map. This is a relief map of South America.

South America

N

LEGEND

| 5,000m 16,404ft | 3,000m 9,842ft | 2,000m 6,562ft | 1,000m 3281ft | 500m 1640ft | 100m 328ft | Sea Level | Below Sea Level |

rice paddy: (rys PAD-ee) *n.* A specially irrigated or flooded field where rice is grown. Rice paddies are very common in Asia.

FUN FACTS

Wet-rice farming is common in Asia. Most rice farmers still use the same methods that were used 2,000 years ago. They break up the soil by hand with tools such as hoes and spades. Sometimes, they use a plow pulled by water buffalo, horses, or oxen.

40

"Nature has been for me, as long as I remember, a source of solace, inspiration, adventure, and delight…"

—Lorraine Anderson, 1988

river: (RIV-ur) *n.* A large, natural stream of water that empties into an ocean, lake, sea, or other body of water. Rivers provide water for many different animals, including human beings.

🔻 FUN FACTS 🔻

The United States has more than 10,000 miles of rivers.

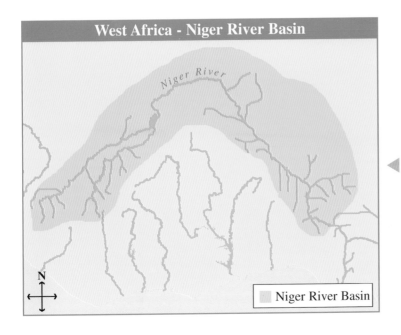

West Africa - Niger River Basin

Niger River

N

☐ Niger River Basin

river basin: (RIV-ur BAY-sun) *n.* An area of land that contains a river and all the streams that flow into it. By the late 1400s, the Songhai of West Africa created an empire that dominated the Niger River Basin.

"[The savannah has] grass which rises to heights of 12 feet overhead and shuts in the narrow trails…with here and there a few low trees all but hidden from view."

—Preston E. James, 1930

Sahel: (SAH-hul) *n.* The flat, dry grasslands in western Africa between the Sahara desert on the north and the tropical forest areas on the south; this treeless area gets about 4-8 inches of rain a year. This photo shows camels in the Sahel region.

savannah: (suh-VAN-nuh) *n.* An area of flat, treeless grasslands in tropical regions. Some of Africa's great civilizations developed in the savannah region.

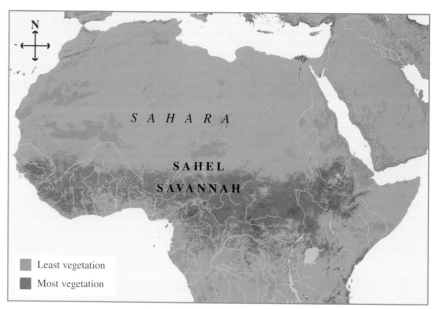

SAHARA

SAHEL

SAVANNAH

N

☐ Least vegetation

■ Most vegetation

scale: (skayl) *n.* A line on a map that shows how the distance between places on a map compares with the real distance between the same places. One part of the scale on this map equals 100 miles.

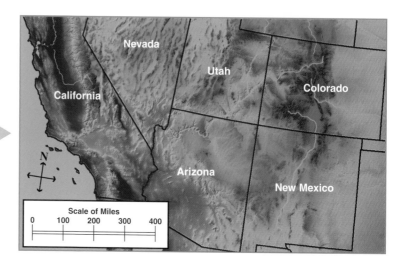

Nevada

Utah

Colorado

California

Arizona

New Mexico

N

Scale of Miles
0   100   200   300   400

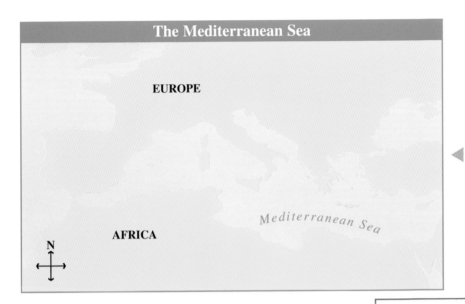

The Mediterranean Sea

EUROPE

Mediterranean Sea

AFRICA

N

sea: (see) *n.* A large body of water, usually salt water, that is either within an ocean or surrounded by land. The ancient Romans created an empire around the Mediterranean Sea.

sea level: (see LEV-ul) *n.* The level of the surface of the ocean. At 282 feet below sea level, Death Valley in California is the lowest spot in the Americas. See DEPTH.

FUN FACTS

The Dead Sea is called "dead" because fish and other sea creatures cannot live in it. They cannot live in the water because it is so salty. The water of the Dead Sea is five times saltier than most sea water.

sea level

"The voyage of discovery lies not in seeking new horizons, but in seeing with new eyes."
—Marcel Proust (1871-1922)

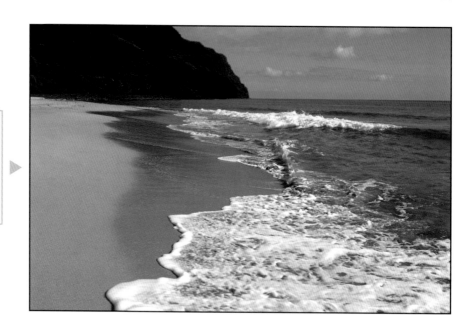

shore: (shohr) *n.* The land bordering a large body of water. Colonists from Europe landed on the shores of North America in the early 1600s. See COAST.

south: (sowth) *n.* A direction indicating the area toward the South Pole. The area at the bottom of a map is usually south.

S

South Pole: (sowth pohl) *n.* The area at the bottom of the earth; the South Pole is 90° south of the equator. Explorers first reached the South Pole in 1911.

South Pole

44

The Roman Empire - A.D. 14

EUROPE

ATLANTIC OCEAN

Black Sea

Mediterranean Sea

AFRICA

Red Sea

N

The Roman Empire - A.D. 14

special purpose map: (SPESH-ul PUR-pus map) *n.* A drawing of an area or region that shows special information such as weather, population, or historical boundaries. Picture symbols are often used on special purpose maps. This special purpose map shows the size of the Roman Empire in A.D. 14.

steppe: (step) *n.* A plain with few or no trees. From early times, groups of nomads have lived in the steppe region of northern China.

PORTUGAL

SPAIN

ATLANTIC OCEAN

Mediterranean Sea

AFRICA

N

strait: (strayt) *n.* A narrow passage of water joining two larger bodies of water. The Strait of Gibraltar connects the Atlantic Ocean and the Mediterranean Sea. See CHANNEL.

45

stratified site: (STRAT-uh-fyd syt) **n.** A place where archaeologists dig into the earth to expose layers of materials. This is a stratified site in Africa where Mary and Louis Leakey found fossils of prehistoric peoples.

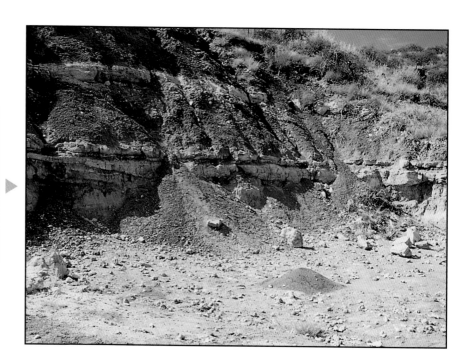

street map: (street map) **n.** A map that shows streets and such things as rivers and parks. A street map is handy to have in order to find your way around a city or town.

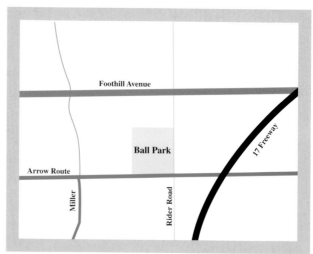

subcontinent: (SUB-KAHN-tuh-nent) **n.** A large piece of land, somewhat separated but still a part of a continent. India is a subcontinent of Asia.

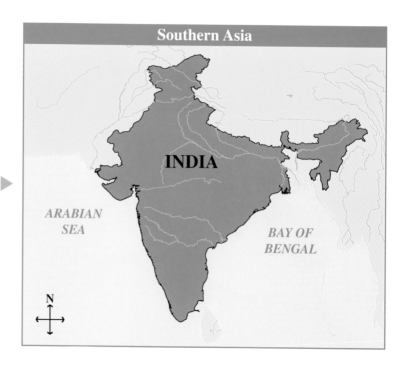

46

Boundaries of the Tectonic Plates

N

Tectonic plate boundaries

tectonic plate: (tek-TON-ik playt) *n.* A large piece of the earth's crust. Tectonic plates that bump into each other cause earthquakes.

FUN FACTS

Millions of years ago, the land of the earth formed one supercontinent, Pangea. Over time, Pangea broke apart into separate tectonic plates. Tectonic plates are always moving slowly in different directions. (They move from 1 inch to 6 inches per year—about how fast your fingernails grow!)

PANGEA

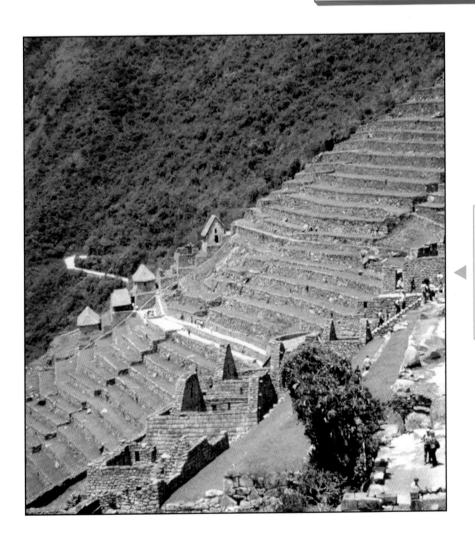

terrace: (TER-is) *n.* A flat, narrow piece of ground cut into a steep slope; usually to create flat land for farming. Farmers cut terraces into hillsides to create more farm land.

topographic map: (top-oh-GRAF-ik map) *n.* A map that uses lines to show the elevation of natural features (such as hills and valleys) of the earth. A topographic map is one kind of physical map. This topographic map illustrates a way to show elevation.

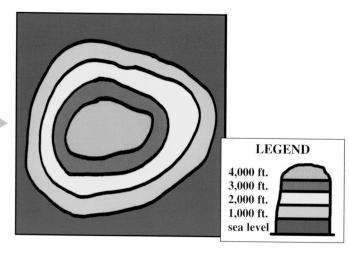

LEGEND

4,000 ft.
3,000 ft.
2,000 ft.
1,000 ft.
sea level

trade winds: (trayd windz) *n.* A system of winds that always blows in the same direction; in the Northern Hemisphere, the trade winds (called the "northeast trade winds") blow from the northeast; in the Southern Hemisphere, the trade winds (called the "southeast trade winds") blow from the southeast. Since early times, sailors have relied on the trade winds to help them sail quickly across the ocean. See OCEAN CURRENTS.

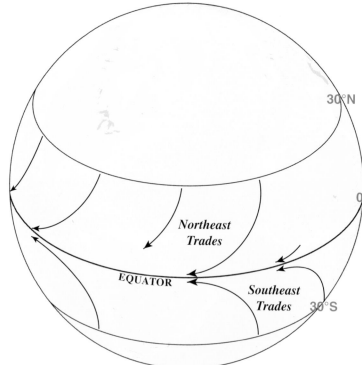

30°N

0°

Northeast Trades

EQUATOR

Southeast Trades 30°S

tributary: (TRIB-yuh-tayr-ee) *n.* A small river (or stream) that flows into a larger river. From this picture you can see a river and one of its tributaries.

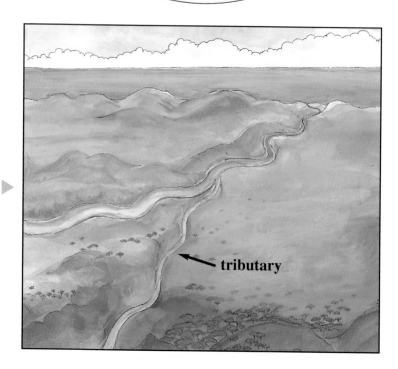

tributary

🌐 *Voices in Geography* 🌐

"…the best map to aid the geographer in forecasting settlement in a new country is one of the natural vegetation."

—Griffith Taylor, 1937

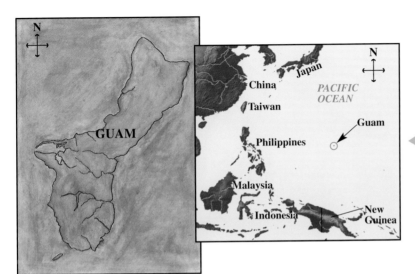

GUAM

Japan
China
Taiwan

PACIFIC
OCEAN

Guam

Philippines

Malaysia

Indonesia

New
Guinea

United States territory: (yoo-NYT-id stayts TAYR-uh-tor-ee) *n.* A part of the United States that has an appointed governor and its own legislature (law-making group), but is not a state. Guam is a United States territory.

valley: (VAL-ee) *n.* Low land between hills or mountains. It is usually warmer in valleys because the hills or mountains block the winds. See RAVINE and GORGE.

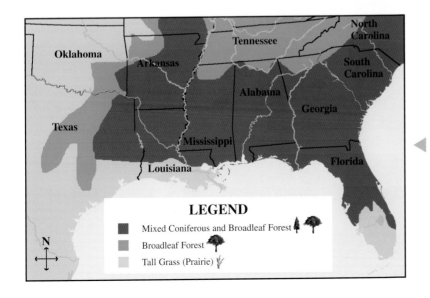

Oklahoma
Tennessee
North Carolina
Arkansas
South Carolina
Alabama
Georgia
Texas
Mississippi
Florida
Louisiana

LEGEND
- Mixed Coniferous and Broadleaf Forest
- Broadleaf Forest
- Tall Grass (Prairie)

vegetation map: (vej-uh-TAY-shun map) *n.* A map that shows plant life such as forest, woodland, scrub, grassland, and desert. This vegetation map shows the kinds of trees and grassland found in the southeastern United States.

volcano: (vall-KAY-noh) *n.*
A hole in the earth's crust
through which hot ashes or
lava (melted rock) come out.
The Hawaiian Islands were
formed by volcanoes.

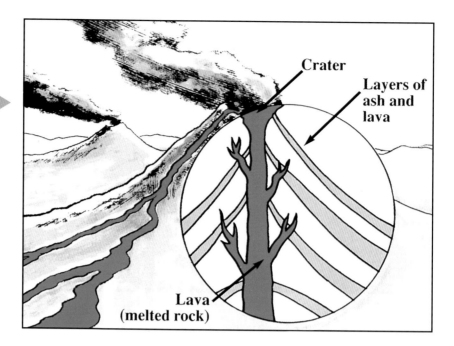

Crater

Layers of
ash and
lava

Lava
(melted rock)

waterfall: (WAHT-ur-fahl) *n.*
A steep fall of water from a
stream or river. In the 1800s,
American factory owners in
the Northeast took advantage
of waterfalls as a source of
power for their machines.
See CATARACT and RAPIDS.

 FUN FACTS

The tallest waterfall in the world is Angel
Falls in Venezuela. It is 3,212 feet high. Do
you know how long it takes for the water to
drop? Count slowly from 1 to 14. That's
about how long it takes for water at the top
of the waterfall to reach the bottom!

weather: (WETH-ur) *n.* The
day-to-day changes in
temperature and rainfall.
Weather has an important
influence on people's lives.
See CLIMATE.

MON	TUE	WED	THU	FRI
Sunny	Partly Cloudy	Mostly Cloudy, Rainy	Mostly Cloudy	Partly Cloudy
High 64°F	High 61°F	High 49°F	High 55°F	High 62°F
Low 49°F	Low 39°F	Low 33°F	Low 42°F	Low 48°F

Appendix I: Geographical Features and Terms in Spanish

Visit www.ballard-tighe.com/geography.htm to find translations of the features and terms in other languages.

agriculture, industry, and resources map: agricultura, industria y mapa de recursos
aqueduct: acueducto
archipelago: archipiélago
atlas: guía de carreteras y mapas, atlas
bay: angra, bahía
boundary: límite, línea limítrofe
canal: canal
canyon: cañón
cape: cabo
cataract: catarata
cave: cueva, caverna
channel: canal
city: ciudad
cliff: risco, acantilado
climate: clima
coast: costa
commercial harbor: puerto comercial
compass rose: rosa de los vientos
continent: continente
Continental Divide: División Continental
dam: embalse, represa
degree: grado
delta: delta
demographic change: cambio demográfico
depth: profundidad
desert: desierto
earthquake: terremoto
elevation: elevación, altitud
environmental pollution: contaminación ambiental
equator: ecuador, línea ecuatorial
erosion: erosión
Fertile Crescent: El Valle del Tigris y Eufrates
flood plain: área de inundación
foothill: estribaciones
forest: selva, bosque
frontier: frontera
gap: hondanada
gazetteer: diccionario geográfico
geographer: geógrafo
geography: geografía
glacier: glaciar

globe: globo, mapamundo
gorge: cañón, barranco
Great Lakes: Grandes Lagos
gulf: golfo
harbor: puerto
hemisphere: hemisferio
hill: cerro, loma
inlet: acceso, ensenada
international date line: línea de cambio de fecha
irrigation systems: sistema de irrigación
island: isla
isle: isla
isthmus: istmo
lake: lago
land bridge: puente
landmark: hito, mojón, señal
landmass: gran extensión
latitude: latitud
legend: epígrafe
loess highlands: montaña fertilizada por el viento
longitude: longitud
map: mapa
marsh: pantano
mesa: meseta
mountain: montaña, monte
mountain pass: paso montañoso
mountain range: cordillera, montañas
natural boundary: límite natural
natural resources: recursos naturales
north: norte
North Pole: Polo Norte
oasis: oasis
ocean: océano
ocean currents: corrientes oceánicas
peninsula: península
physical map: mapa físico
piedmont: tierras bajas
plain: llano, campo
planet: planeta
plateau: altiplano
political map: mapa político
population: población

population map: mapa de población
port: puerto
prime meridian: meridiano de Greenwich
rain forest: bosque húmedo, bosque lluvioso
rapid: rápidos
ravine: barranco
region: región
relief map: mapa de relieve
rice paddy: cultivo de arroz, arrozal
river: río
river basin: cuenca del río, lecho fluvial
Sahel: Sahara árido
savannah: sabana, llano
scale: escala
sea: mar
sea level: nivel del mar
shore: orilla, playa
south: sur
South Pole: Polo Sur
special purpose map: mapa especializado
steppe: estepa
strait: estrecho
stratified site: área de cultivo
street map: mapa de carreteras o rutas
subcontinent: subcontinente
tectonic plate: placa tectónica
terrace: terraza, hilera
topographic map: mapa de topografía, mapa topográfico
trade winds: vientos alisios, vientos generales
tributary: afluente, tributario
United States territory: territorio de Estados Unidos (de América)
valley: cuenca, valle
vegetation map: mapa de vegetación
volcano: volcán
waterfall: cascada, catarata
weather: tiempo, clima

Appendix II: Political Map of the United States

ATLANTIC OCEAN

GULF OF MEXICO

PACIFIC OCEAN

ARCTIC OCEAN

BERING SEA

CANADA

MEXICO

★ State capitals

Scale of Miles
0 200 400

N

States and capitals:

Maine — Augusta ★
New Hampshire — Concord ★
Vermont — Montpelier ★
Massachusetts — Boston ★
Rhode Island — Providence ★
Connecticut — Hartford ★
New York — Albany ★
New Jersey — Trenton ★
Delaware — Dover ★
Maryland — Annapolis ★
Washington, D.C.
Pennsylvania — Harrisburg ★
West Virginia — Charleston ★
Virginia — Richmond ★
North Carolina — Raleigh ★
South Carolina — Columbia ★
Georgia — Atlanta ★
Florida — Tallahassee ★
Ohio — Columbus ★
Michigan — Lansing ★
Indiana — Indianapolis ★
Kentucky — Frankfort ★
Tennessee — Nashville ★
Alabama — Montgomery ★
Mississippi — Jackson ★
Wisconsin — Madison ★
Illinois — Springfield ★
Minnesota — St. Paul ★
Iowa — Des Moines ★
Missouri — Jefferson City ★
Arkansas — Little Rock ★
Louisiana — Baton Rouge ★
North Dakota — Bismarck ★
South Dakota — Pierre ★
Nebraska — Lincoln ★
Kansas — Topeka ★
Oklahoma — Oklahoma City ★
Texas — Austin ★
Montana — Helena ★
Wyoming — Cheyenne ★
Colorado — Denver ★
New Mexico — Santa Fe ★
Utah — Salt Lake City ★
Arizona — Phoenix ★
Idaho — Boise ★
Washington — Olympia ★
Oregon — Salem ★
Nevada — Carson City ★
California — Sacramento ★
Hawaii — Honolulu ★
Alaska — Juneau ★

Lakes and rivers:
Lake Ontario, Lake Erie, Lake Huron, Lake Michigan, Lake Superior, Mississippi River, Missouri River, Arkansas River, Colorado River, Rio Grande River

Hawaii
PACIFIC OCEAN
Miles 0 100

Alaska
Miles 0 1000

Appendix III: Relief Map of the United States

Appendix IV: World Map & Statistics

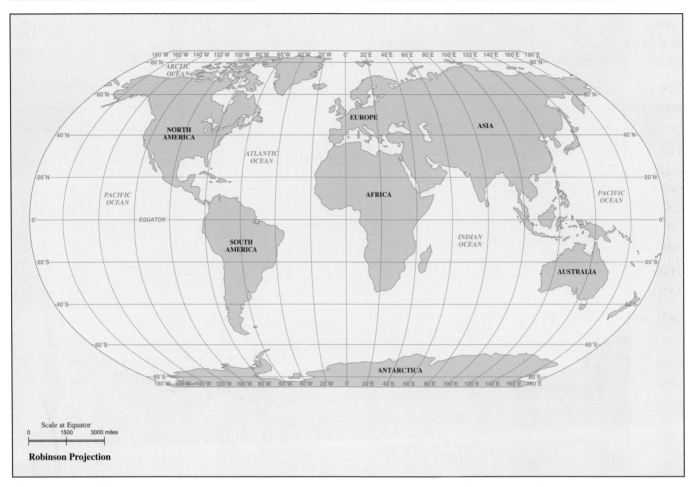

Scale at Equator
0   1500   3000 miles

Robinson Projection

Longest Rivers	Length in miles
Nile, Africa	4,145
Amazon, South America	4,007
Mississippi-Missouri-Red Rock, U.S.A.	3,710
Chang Jiang (Yangtze), China	3,500
Ob'-Irtysh, Russia-Kazakhstan	3,362
Yenisey-Angara, Asia	3,100
Huang He (Yellow), China	2,950

Oceans and Major Seas	Area in square miles
Pacific Ocean	63,855,000
Atlantic Ocean	31,744,000
Indian Ocean	28,417,000
Arctic Ocean	5,427,000
Caribbean Sea	970,000
Mediterranean Sea	969,000
South China Sea	895,000

Highest Mountains	Height in feet
Everest, Nepal-China	29,028
K2 (Godwin Austen), Pakistan-China	28,250
Kanchenjunga, Nepal-India	28,208
Lhotse, Nepal-China	27,923
Makalu, Nepal-China	27,789
Dhaulagiri, Nepal	26,810
Nanga Parbat, Pakistan	26,660

Major Lakes	Area in square miles
Caspian Sea, Asia	143,243
Lake Superior, U.S.A.-Canada	31,820
Lake Victoria, Africa	26,628
Lake Huron, U.S.A.-Canada	23,010
Lake Michigan, U.S.A.	22,400
Aral Sea, Kazakhstan-Uzbekistan	15,830
Lake Tanganyika, Africa	12,650

(Source: *New Century World Atlas*, 2000)

A Note to Teachers and Parents

Geography explains history. Historical events are inextricably tied to the physical location and resources of a place. Imagine the study of ancient Egypt without understanding the role the Nile River played in the entire existence of that civilization.

The purpose of the *Explore Geography Picture Dictionary* is to give students a foundation of basic geographical facts that will help them to understand their world and their history. The history of a place just makes more sense when we understand its geography.

The *Explore Geography Picture Dictionary* is easy to use. Entries are organized alphabetically and each includes a definition, sentence, and picture. To make it easier to access this information, there is also an index at the back of the book. The pronunciation* of each entry also is given. If a word used in the definition has its own entry, it is printed in red type. In some cases examples are given of a word; those are found in parentheses after the word. The "Fun Facts" and "Voices in Geography" sections provide more information, as well as quotations related to the geographic terms.

The *Explore Geography Picture Dictionary* can be used on its own or in conjunction with the *Explore* social studies series.**

Help students learn how to use the *Explore Geography Picture Dictionary* by using activities like these:

- *Find the Geographic Feature—FAST!* Ask students to find examples of a geographic feature such as *lake* or *mountain*. Each student notes his or her starting and finishing times. Students attempt to beat their own times.

- *What's the Connection?* Students choose an entry in the *Explore Geography Picture Dictionary* that has a link to another entry, and then explain the connection. For example, the entry for "degree" says, "See equator and prime meridian," because the equator is at zero degrees latitude, and the prime meridian is at zero degrees longitude.

Internet Links to Geography Activities

Please visit **www.ballard-tighe.com/geography.htm** for links to geography activity sheets you can download. These activities correlate to the *Explore* programs and will help you use the *Explore Geography Picture Dictionary*. They also will help your students become familiar with the themes and standards set forth by the Joint Committee on Geographic Education of the National Council for Geographic Education (NCGE) and the Association of American Geographers (AAG). Also available at this web site are links to Korean, Arabic, and other translations of the geographical features and terms.

---

* Pronunciations are derived from the following three sources: *American Heritage Dictionary of the English Language*, 1981; *Oxford American Dictionary: Heald Colleges Edition*, 1982; *Webster's New World College Dictionary, Third Edition*, 1990.

** The *Explore* social studies series teaches mainstream, grade-level content using a variety of learning strategies and techniques to help all students, including English language learners, access the core curriculum. The textbooks are full of pictures and visuals that help make the material comprehensible. The text is clear and easy to understand. In addition, the teacher's guide offers a broad range of activities that involve and interest students. The *Explore Geography Picture Dictionary* is a special addition to the *Explore* series.

Index

The definition of the word is found on the page printed in red.

agriculture, industry, and resources map 5, 29
Africa 6, 8, 12, 16, 21, 27, 39, 41, 42, 46, 54
Antarctica 12
aqueduct 5, 25
archipelago 6, 25, 26
Asia 12, 25, 27, 30, 40, 46, 54
atlas 6
Australia 12
bay 6
boundary 7, 32, 37, 45
canal 7, 25, 26
canyon 7, 36, 39
cape 8
cataract 8, 39, 50
cave 9
channel 9, 45
city 5, 9, 22, 37, 46
cliff 10
climate 10, 50
coast 8, 11, 26, 44
commercial harbor 11, 22
compass rose 11
continent 12, 16, 25, 27, 34, 46
Continental Divide 12
dam 13, 25
degree 13, 28, 29, 38
delta 13
demographic change 14
depth 14, 43
desert 14, 33, 36, 42, 49
earthquake 15, 47
east 11, 12, 23, 24, 29, 34, 38, 39, 49, 50
elevation 15, 30, 48
environmental pollution 16
equator 13, 16, 23, 28, 33, 44
erosion 16
Europe 9, 12, 18, 30, 32, 34, 44
Fertile Crescent 17
flood plain 17
foothill 18, 23
forest 18, 39, 42, 49
frontier 18
gap 19, 31, 39
gazetteer 19

geographer 20, 49
geography 5, 10, 17, 20, 24, 36
glacier 21
globe 21
gorge 21, 39, 49
Great Lakes 22
gulf 17, 22
harbor 11, 22, 38
hemisphere 16, 23, 38, 48
hill 9, 18, 19, 23, 30, 40, 47-49
inlet 24
international date line 24
irrigation systems 5, 7, 13, 25
island 6, 25, 26, 50
isle 25, 26
isthmus 26
lake 7, 14, 22, 24, 26, 41, 54
land bridge 27
landmark 27
landmass 12, 27
latitude 13, 16, 28
legend 28
loess highlands 28
longitude 13, 28, 29, 38
map 5, 6, 10-12, 21, 25, 28, 29, 32, 35, 37, 38, 40, 42, 44, 45, 46, 48, 49
marsh 29
mesa 30
mountain 12, 15, 18-19, 23, 27, 30-32, 35, 49, 54
mountain pass 19, 31, 39
mountain range 31, 32
natural boundary 32
natural resources 5, 32
north 11, 12, 16, 23, 24, 27, 28, 30, 32, 33, 38, 39, 42, 44, 45, 50
North America 11, 12, 27, 30, 44
North Pole 24, 32, 33, 38
oasis 33
ocean 6, 12, 14, 22, 24, 25, 27, 34, 41, 43, 45, 48, 54
ocean currents 34
peninsula 8, 34
physical map 35, 40, 48
piedmont 18, 23, 35
plain 17, 28, 35, 45

planet 29, 36
plateau 36
political map 29, 37
population 14, 37, 38, 45
population map 29, 38
port 22, 38
prime meridian 13, 23, 28, 29, 38
rain forest 39
rapid 8, 39, 50
ravine 19, 39, 49
region 14, 18, 20, 29, 35, 37, 39, 40, 42, 45
relief map 29, 35, 40
rice paddy 40
river 6-8, 12, 13, 17, 21, 24, 28, 32, 39, 41, 46, 48, 50, 54
river basin 41
Sahel 42
savannah 42
scale 42
sea 8, 14-15, 17, 22, 30, 34, 41, 43, 45, 46, 54
sea level 14, 15, 30, 43
shore 44
south 11, 12, 16, 23, 24, 28, 30, 36, 38, 40, 42, 44, 49
South America 12, 15, 40, 54
South Pole 24, 38, 44
special purpose map 45
steppe 45
strait 9, 45
stratified site 46
street map 29, 46
subcontinent 46
tectonic plate 15, 47
terrace 47
topographic map 35, 48
trade winds 48
tributary 48
United States territory 49
valley 7, 28, 39, 40, 43, 48, 49
vegetation map 29, 49
volcano 15, 25, 50
waterfall 8, 39, 50
weather 10, 31, 45, 50
west 7, 8, 11, 12, 23, 24, 29, 30, 34, 36, 38, 40, 41